THE MUSEUM!

Come and have a look!

Buried treasure

Ancient Romans

Dinosaurs

Gift shop and café

This mummy is hiding inside the book. Can you find him in every scene?

Spot the MUMMY in the Museum

Sarah Khan

Illustrated by
Peter Bull Art Studio

QED

WELCOME TO

There's lots to see.

Ancient Greeks

Vikings

Masks

Ancient Egyptians

The Americas

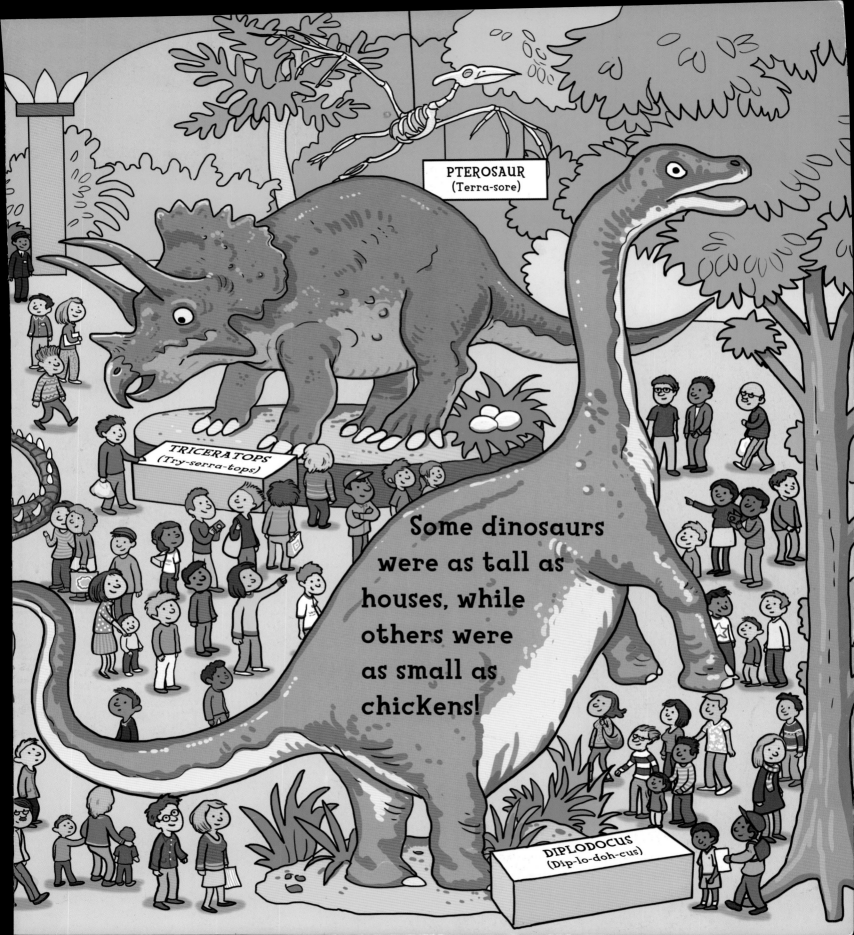

PTEROSAUR
(Terra-sore)

TRICERATOPS
(Try-serra-tops)

Some dinosaurs were as tall as houses, while others were as small as chickens!

DIPLODOCUS
(Dip-lo-doh-cus)

The rulers of Ancient Egypt loved gold. They rode in gold chariots and were even buried in gold coffins.

Can you spot these things?

sad mask teddy bear horse statue shield torch

ROMAN POTTERY

GOLD NECKLACE

VIKING AXES

GREEK VASE

VIKING SWORDS

Many precious and ancient things become lost in the ground. Scientists hunt for this buried treasure to understand the past.

ROMAN CUPS

ANCIENT JEWELLERY

FOSSILS

DECORATIVE HORNS

ANCIENT CARVING

DINOSAUR TOOTH

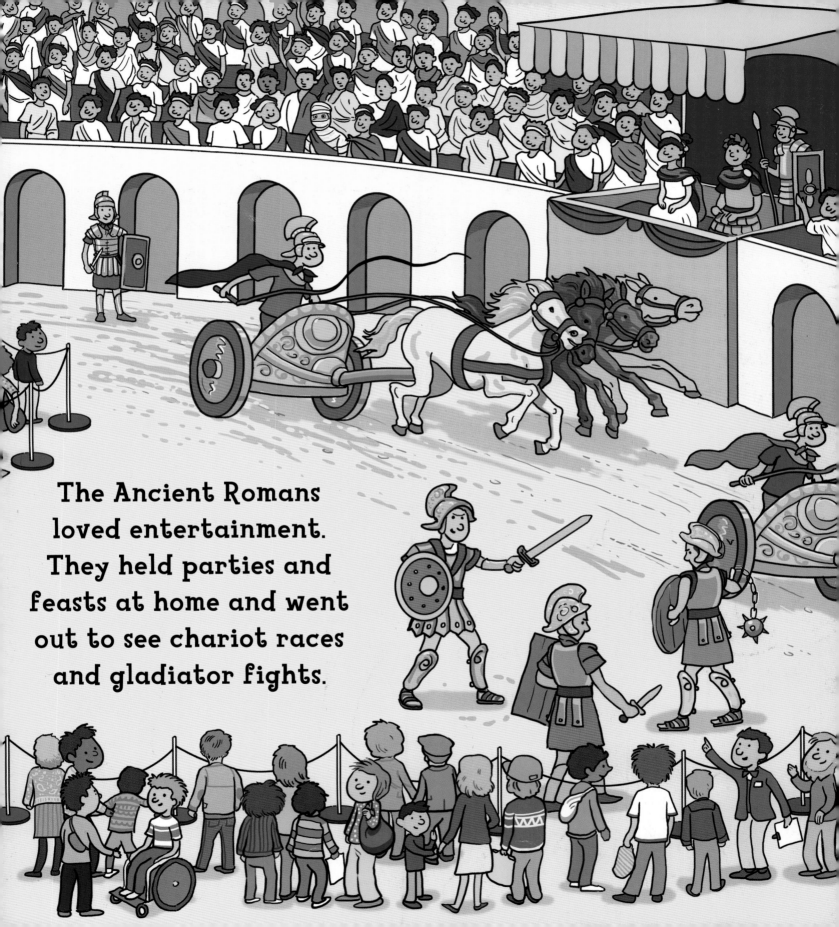

The Ancient Romans loved entertainment. They held parties and feasts at home and went out to see chariot races and gladiator fights.

Can you spot these things?

gold
vase

dream
catcher

gold
bracelet

bow

plate

EUROPE

AUSTRALASIA

ASIA

There are many different types of masks. The oldest mask ever discovered was found in a desert near Jerusalem. It is made of stone and is more than 9000 years old!

Can you spot these things?

dragon head   carrots   boots   bird   crossed axes

The Vikings lived over a thousand years ago. They were good at farming and sailing. They travelled to different countries all over Europe in boats called longships.

Which shield do you like the best?

Some museums are free to enter, but sell food and gifts. The money they make from this helps them stay open.

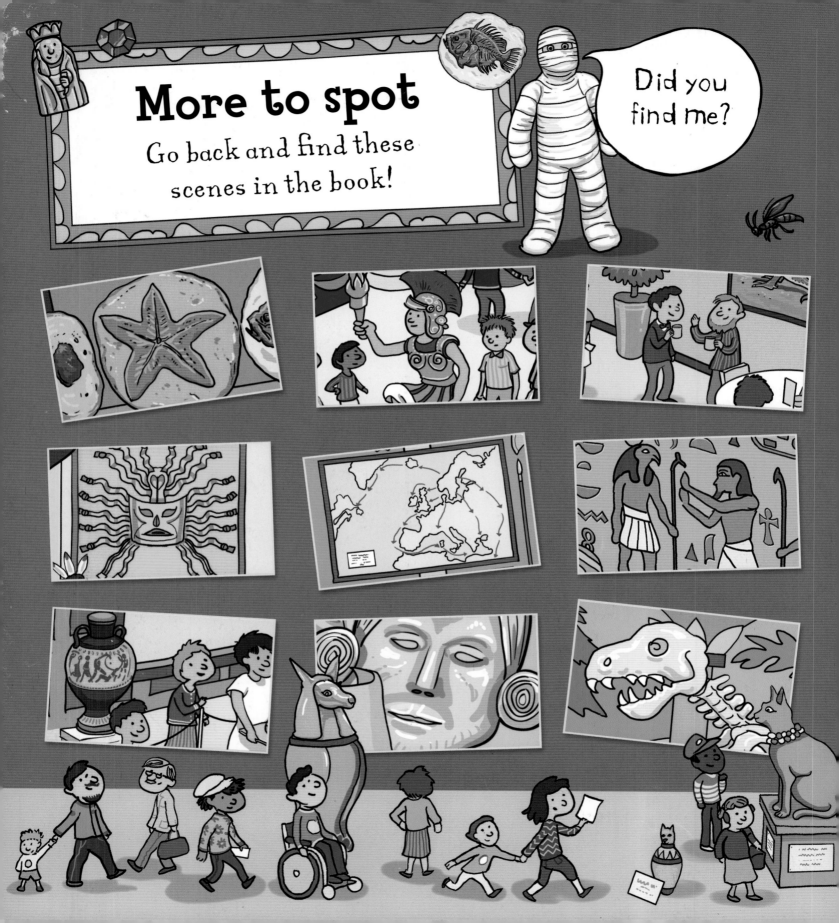

More to spot

Go back and find these scenes in the book!

Did you find me?

Did you Know?

The word dinosaur comes from the Greek language and means 'terrible lizard'.

Ancient Romans loved eating exotic things like swans, crows, horses, peacocks and dormice.

Some of the first people to wear jewellery were men. They wore chains and bracelets to show how rich they were and to bring them luck in battle.

The ancient people of Mexico believed in worshipping the sun to give it enough strength to rise each day.

The Ancient Egyptians invented lots of things we use today, such as paper, pens, locks, keys and even toothpaste!

More museum fun!

Make a Viking shield

Find a large piece of cardboard and ask an adult to cut it into a round or oval shape. Paint or use crayons to decorate one side in your Viking design. Then, once it's dry, stick a strip of cardboard on the back to make a loop for your arm to hold the shield.

Buried treasure

Choose a cuddly toy that you can hide around your home for a friend or family member to spot, just like the mummy in this book! You could hide other objects too and make a list of things to find.

Museum visit

Ask an adult if there is a museum near you, then see if you can go on a trip to visit it. Many museums have events especially for children and are free. Take a sketchbook and draw some of your favourite objects.

Make a mask

Ask an adult to help you cut eye and mouth holes in a paper plate, then make two small holes on either side and tie the ends of a piece of string to each hole. Choose one of the masks in the book to copy or create your own mask design!

Quarto Knows

Quarto is the authority on a wide range of topics.
Quarto educates, entertains and enriches the lives of our readers—enthusiasts and lovers of hands-on living.
www.quartoknows.com

Design: Duck Egg Blue and Mike Henson
Editors: Tasha Percy and Sophie Hallam
Editorial Director: Victoria Garrard
Art Director: Laura Roberts-Jensen

First published in the UK in 2015 by
QED Publishing
Part of The Quarto Group
The Old Brewery,
6 Blundell Street, London, N7 9BH

A catalogue record for this book is available from the British Library.

ISBN 978 1 78493 092 9

Printed in China